SPECTRUM
for VIOLIN

16 contemporary pieces

Compiled by Alexandra Wood

ABRSM

CONTENTS

* with accompanying soundtrack

First published in 2009 by ABRSM (Publishing) Ltd,
a wholly owned subsidiary of ABRSM
24 Portland Place, London W1B 1LU, United Kingdom

This collection © 2009 by The Associated Board of the Royal Schools of Music

ISBN 978 1 86096 748 1

Cover design by Økvik Design. Music extract from manuscript of
A Fork in the Road by David Sawer. Music origination by Andrew Jones.
Printed in England by Caligraving Ltd, Thetford, Norfolk.

INTRODUCTION

Spectrum for Violin has arrived!

It has been a long but an amazing and thoroughly rewarding journey, and I feel privileged to have been involved. I have enjoyed every moment, from the initial stages of inviting the composers to contribute to this volume, through to the excitement of receiving the very first piece – and the last (I shan't name any names!).

More recently, Thalia Myers and I spent a glorious few days working on the pieces with the composers in preparation for the recording. Some serious timetabling enabled this to be done face to face in most cases, but in a few instances via email, Skype and even the old-fashioned way – down the telephone! It was indeed a luxury to be able to discuss the music with the composers, but the recording is in no way meant to be the 'definitive' performance: more an informed, personal interpretation. It is up to the performer (and teacher) to take the score, and bring it to life by making it his or her own.

The end result is, I hope, a wonderful kaleidoscope of miniatures, each equally at home in the teaching room or on the concert platform. I believe that there really is a little something for everyone here, from the very beginner to the seasoned performer alike: a gem for those that love to spin a melody, or an opportunity for the performer to mingle with electronic sounds; a piece for a true violin/piano duo where both players are challenged, or the chance for the violinist to take centre stage.

My thanks go to our 16 composers for their hard work. They responded to the *Spectrum* brief with great enthusiasm, professionalism and of course tremendous skill. I am immensely grateful to Leslie East and Rosie Cousins at ABRSM for their commitment, patience and keen eyes and ears. My thanks also to sound engineer Ken Blair, who helped ease us through the recording process. But above all I would like to thank Thalia for all her support, advice and encouragement, and without whom we would not be blessed with the phenomenon that is *Spectrum*.

Enjoy!

Alexandra Wood
June 2009

COMPOSER BIOGRAPHIES

PHILIP CASHIAN

b. 1963 Manchester. Studied at Cardiff University and at the Guildhall School of Music & Drama with Oliver Knussen and Simon Bainbridge; also with Lukas Foss at Tanglewood. Won Mendelssohn Scholarship, 1991, and Britten Prize, 1992. Currently Head of Composition at the Royal Academy of Music. Works are performed and broadcast worldwide and include orchestral, chamber, vocal and instrumental music as well as opera and music for amateur musicians and children. *Dark Inventions*, a CD of his chamber music, released 2001.

TANSY DAVIES

b. 1973 Bristol. Studied composition and French horn at Colchester Institute; later, whilst freelancing professionally in orchestras and rock bands, studied composition with Simon Bainbridge at the Guildhall School of Music & Drama and subsequently with Simon Holt at Royal Holloway College, London (currently Composer in Residence). Her music, which includes works for orchestra, ensemble and multi-media, is informed by both classical avant-garde and experimental rock; also influenced by the natural world and the architecture of Zaha Hadid. Recent commissions from the Aldeburgh Festival, Birmingham Contemporary Music Group, Britten Sinfonia and BBC Proms.

DANIEL GIORGETTI

b. 1971 London. Studied at the London College of Music with Martin Ellerby and at the Royal College of Music with Edwin Roxburgh. Awards and prizes include Worshipful Company of Musicians' Silver Medal and Young Composers' Award at Huddersfield Festival; also finalist in Queen Elisabeth International Competition for Composers, Belgium. Works are performed and broadcast in Europe and the USA. Output includes orchestral and chamber music, works for voice and solo instruments and music for film and television.

MICHAEL ZEV GORDON

b. 1963 London. Studied composition at Cambridge with Robin Holloway and subsequently with Oliver Knussen, Franco Donatoni and Louis Andriessen. Plays the oboe. Has taught composition at the Royal Northern College of Music, Durham University and University of Birmingham. Presently Senior Lecturer in Composition at the University of Southampton, and teaches composition at the Royal College of Music. Works are widely performed and broadcast; has received, among other awards, a Prix Italia in 2004 for radio composition *A Pebble in the Pond* and a British Composer Award in 2008 for choral *This Night*. Instrumental output includes works for chamber ensembles and solo instruments.

HELEN GRIME

b. 1981 Edinburgh. Attended City of Edinburgh Music School and St Mary's Music School, Edinburgh. Later studied oboe and composition at the Royal College of Music, London, and at the Tanglewood Music Center. Subsequently held the Legal & General Junior Fellowship at the RCM for two years. Composition teachers have included Julian Anderson and Edwin Roxburgh. Won Making Music Award at 2003 British Composer Awards for Oboe Concerto. Commissions in 2009 from, among others, the Tanglewood Music Center and Birmingham Contemporary Music Group. Output includes music theatre, and works for orchestra, chamber ensembles and solo instruments.

KENNETH HESKETH

b. 1968 Liverpool. Composed from early youth. Studied at the Royal College of Music, and then at Tanglewood with Henri Dutilleux. Subsequently awarded a scholarship from the Toepfer Foundation, Hamburg, at the behest of Sir Simon Rattle. New Music Fellow at Kettle's Yard, Cambridge, 2003–5. Now lives in London and is a professor at the RCM and at Liverpool University. Receives many commissions from major performing organizations in Europe, Canada and the USA. In 2006 Susanna Mälkki chose his work *Netsuke* for her opening concert as Music Director of Ensemble Intercontemporain. In 2007 he was made Composer in the House with the Royal Liverpool Philharmonic Orchestra. Output includes works in all genres, from solo to opera.

DAVID MATTHEWS

b. 1943 London. Read Classics at University of Nottingham and afterwards studied composition privately with Anthony Milner. Also learned much from Benjamin Britten (to whom he was an assistant at Aldeburgh in the late 1960s), Nicholas Maw and Peter Sculthorpe. Has written a great variety of music from symphonies (six so far and a seventh in progress) to chamber music (including 11 string quartets). His Fifth and Sixth Symphonies were premiered at the BBC Proms. Many works have been recorded. Has also written books on Tippett and Britten.

THEA MUSGRAVE

b. 1928 Barnton, Midlothian. Studied first at the University of Edinburgh and later as a pupil of Nadia Boulanger in Paris. In 1970 was a Guest Professor at the University of California, Santa Barbara. Later, from 1978–2002, was Distinguished Professor at Queens College, City University of New York. Has resided in the USA since 1972. In 1974 received the Koussevitzky Award, resulting in the composition of *Space Play*; has also been awarded two Guggenheim Fellowships (1974–5 and 1982–3). Has received several Honorary Degrees both in the USA and UK. Output includes ten operas, mostly to her own librettos; also ballets, orchestral works including concertos, and chamber, solo vocal and choral repertoire. Receives numerous commissions from the UK and USA. Recurrent, though by no means exclusive themes in her work are her native Scotland and, on occasion, the historic role of women: Mary Queen of Scots, Harriet Tubman.

PATRICK NUNN

b. 1969 Tunbridge Wells. Studied composition with Frank Denyer at Dartington College of Arts, Gary Carpenter at the Royal Welsh College of Music & Drama and with Simon Bainbridge and Jonathan Harvey whilst completing his PhD in composition at the Royal Academy of Music (funded by a PRS Scholarship). Has been the recipient of many prizes and awards including the BBC Radio 3 Composing for Children prize for *Songs of Our Generation* (1995), a British Composer Award for *Mercurial Sparks, Volatile Shadows* (2006) and the Alan Bush prize for *Transilient Fragments* (2008). His music, encompassing a wide range of mainly instrumental and electroacoustic, has been performed throughout the UK and on the continent and has featured at over 40 festivals worldwide. Has written and worked with a diverse range of collaborators including Piano Circus, Icebreaker, Ballet Rambert, The Gogmagogs, and the New London Children's Choir.

JOÃO PEDRO OLIVEIRA

b. 1959 Lisbon. Studied composition and organ performance at Gregorian Institute of Lisbon and architecture at Fine Arts School of Lisbon. Later, as Fulbright Scholar with a Gulbenkian Foundation Fellowship, at University of New York, Stony Brook. At University of Aveiro, Portugal, is Senior Professor of Composition and Electronic Music, and Director of Electronic Music Studio. Winner of numerous awards and prizes. Works have been recorded and are internationally performed. Output includes opera and works, with and without electronics, for orchestra, chamber ensembles, solo instruments and voice.

TIMOTHY SALTER

b. 1942 Mexborough, Yorkshire. Read music at St John's College, Cambridge. As pianist, has performed internationally with singers and instrumentalists. Also active as conductor and is Musical Director of The Ionian Singers. Founder and Director of Usk Recordings. Teaches composition and performance studies at the Royal College of Music. Output includes music for orchestra and a wide variety of chamber ensembles; solo instrumental, voice, and choral music.

DAVID SAWER

b. 1961 Stockport. Brought up in Suffolk, and led Suffolk Youth Orchestra. Studied composition, singing and violin at University of York; later studied in Cologne with Mauricio Kagel, whose works he has directed and performed. Teaches composition at the Royal Academy of Music. Has been recipient of Fulbright Fellowship in Composition, Paul Hamlyn Foundation Award and Arts Foundation Composer Fellowship. Has written for orchestra, chamber ensembles and solo instruments; also works for music theatre, dance, film and radio.

HOWARD SKEMPTON

b. 1947 Chester. Studied privately in London with Cornelius Cardew (a significant influence, both as pianist and leading experimentalist). Professional activity has included working in music publishing and playing the accordion. Much of his work is recorded and widely performed. String quartet *Tendrils* won Best Chamber-Scale Composition at the Royal Philharmonic Society Awards in May 2005. Output extends to over 300 works, many of them short 'lyric poems' for piano or accordion; also music for ballet and orchestra, choir, voice and chamber ensembles.

DOBRINKA TABAKOVA

b. 1980 Plovdiv, Bulgaria. Moved to London in 1991. Studied composition at the Junior Academy of the Royal Academy of Music; graduated from the Guildhall School of Music & Drama and received her doctorate from King's College London in 2007. Teachers have included Simon Bainbridge, Diana Burrell, Robert Keeley and Andrew Schultz. Prizes include the Jean-Frédéric Perrenoud Prize and Medal at the fourth Vienna International Music Competition (1995), GSMD Lutosławski Composition Prize (1999), a prize for her anthem *Praise* written for the Queen's Golden Jubilee (and performed at St Paul's Cathedral) and the 2007 KCL Adam Prize. Recent commissions from BBC Radio 3, Royal Philharmonic Society and Amsterdam Sinfonietta. Output includes solo repertoire, chamber music, concertos, orchestral opuses, song cycles, two chamber operas and a collection of choral works.

HUW WATKINS

b. 1976 Pontypool, Monmouthshire. Studied at Cambridge with Robin Holloway and Alexander Goehr, and now teaches composition at the Royal College of Music, London. Commissions include works for the BBC Proms, the London Symphony Orchestra, London Sinfonietta, Birmingham Contemporary Music Group and Nash Ensemble. Has performed his own Piano Concerto with BBC National Orchestra of Wales, and made several recordings including the first recording of Goehr's piano cycle *Symmetry Disorders Reach*. Compositional output includes orchestral, chamber and vocal music, and a one-act opera called *Crime Fiction*.

HUGH WOOD

b. 1932 Parbold, Lancashire. Read history at Oxford then studied privately with W. S. Lloyd Webber, Iain Hamilton and Mátyás Seiber. Taught at Morley College, the Royal Academy of Music, and at Glasgow and Liverpool Universities: then for 22 years at Cambridge, where he was Fellow and Director of Studies in Music at Churchill College, and University Lecturer in Music. Has in the past received many commissions and performances from the BBC, including *Scenes from Comus* (Proms 1965), the Cello Concerto (Proms 1969), the First and Second String Quartets (1962 and 1970) and the Robert Graves song cycle *Wild Cyclamen* (2006). His Second Violin Concerto, written for Alexandra Wood, was performed for the first time on 23 January 2009.

ALEXANDRA WOOD

b. 1977 Maidenhead. Graduated from Selwyn College, Cambridge, with a starred First; went on to the Royal College of Music, London, where she was President Emerita Scholar, and studied violin with Itzhak Rashkovsky. Prizewinner at the Wieniawski and Yampolsky international violin competitions and recipient of the Worshipful Company of Musicians' Medal and a Star Award from the Countess of Munster Trust. Has given recitals in many of the UK's most prestigious venues as well as live on BBC Radio 3, and has been concerto soloist with the Philharmonia, City of London Sinfonia and Orchestra of St John's; has worked with conductors including Pierre Boulez and Oliver Knussen. Her CD of world premiere recordings, *Chimera*, was released in 2005. Regularly leads Birmingham Contemporary Music Group and has guest-led other ensembles including London Sinfonietta. Teaches violin at Birmingham Conservatoire.

A Fork in the Road

DAVID SAWER

London, November 2006

The composer has written: 'A fork in the road is a place where a road or path divides in two. In many folk tales this is often the moment when the main character of the story must make a crucial decision. The piece is best thought of as being one-in-a-bar.'

for my darling boy

Joshi's Dance

MICHAEL ZEV GORDON

London, March 2009

The composer has written: 'This little piece was written for my son Joshi to play. It should sound fun and bouncy in the fast parts and suddenly tender in the slow bars.'

An Alpine Tune

DAVID MATTHEWS

London, October 2007

The composer has written: 'I wrote the melody for *An Alpine Tune* in the Italian Dolomites, near to where Mahler wrote *Das Lied von der Erde* and his last two symphonies. It is an inspiring landscape. I also used the tune in my Sixth Symphony.'

Forgotten Game

PHILIP CASHIAN

London, March 2007

Arietta

HOWARD SKEMPTON

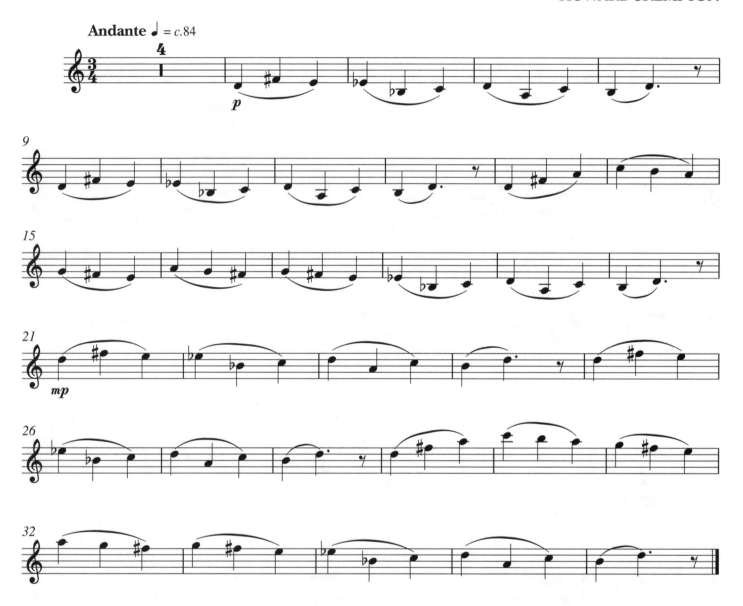

Leamington Spa, September 2007

The composer has written: 'An arietta is a short aria, so this piece is a song without words. The melody should be lyrical and sustained, in contrast to the dry precision of repeated notes for the pianist's left hand.'

AB 3453

Daydream

TIMOTHY SALTER

London, 15–16 June 2007

The composer has written: 'The direction "musing" gives the character of this piece, although a more openly lyrical few bars emerge in the middle. The pizzicati and staccato phrases afford a contrast with the smooth flow of the opening scalic idea.'

AB 3453

Lydian River

DOBRINKA TABAKOVA

Allegro (gentle and flowing) ♪ = *c*.240 (♩. ♩ = *c*.48)

The composer has written: 'This piece is entirely in the Lydian mode (all white keys F to F). Find an Allegro tempo that you are comfortable with, to simulate a gently flowing river. Try to create a very still atmosphere at the start, gradually growing. Louder dynamics should not be forced but warm, enveloping.'

* Play on the string (using the upper middle part of the bow), creating a flowing, legato melody without accents. The sound should resemble that of a folk fiddle.

fading into the distance

Woodman's Echo

TANSY DAVIES

Very lightly ♩ = 120–130

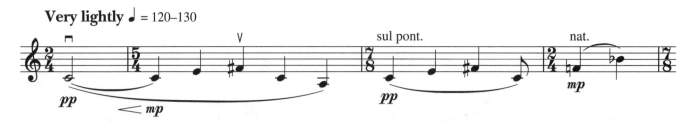

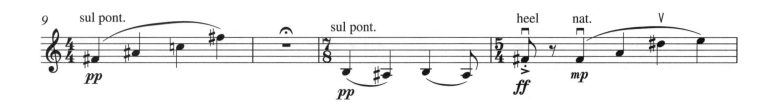

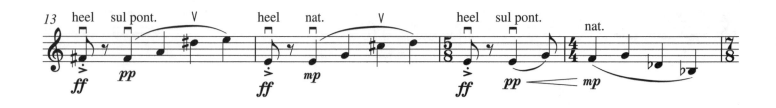

The composer has written: 'The bow changes that occur within phrase marks should be as smooth as possible: each phrase should be like a single exhalation of breath. The short, loud notes at the heel of the bow should be like sharp inhalations.'

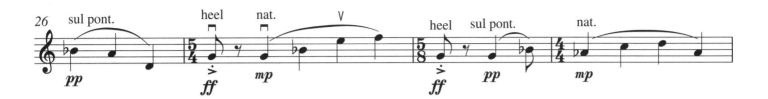

Rochester, March 2007

Bagatelle

HUGH WOOD

London NW5, 6–11 October 2007

The composer has written: 'I hope this piece will encourage rhythmic agility in both players, and strengthen their instinct for instant characterization – the ability to switch quickly from a lyrical passage to a more vigorous one. It needs a very light touch throughout.'

AB 3453

Sarabande

HUW WATKINS

London, January 2007

The composer has written: 'My favourite movements from Bach's suites tend to be the Sarabandes. I wanted to write one of my own, for violin and piano, although the conventional rhythms of this slow dance have been modified and distorted. The harmonies are often quite dissonant and anguished and this should be taken into account in a performance of the piece.'

Collage on D

for violin and soundtrack

PATRICK NUNN

The composer has written: 'Collage on D incorporates a backing track made up of electronically transformed sounds of the violin. This provides a backdrop in which the solo violin can weave, forming part of the overall sound collage.'

Performance directions

 and   Natural harmonic; produced by lightly touching the note at the pitch indicated. (The resulting pitch is shown in brackets.)

    (b. 1) Play the glissando in a manner that allows all the intervening harmonics to sound.

m.s.p.   Change smoothly from one bowing position to the next.
    molto sul ponticello; bow very near the bridge.
n.   Normal bowing position.

ricochet
    (b. 7) Allow the bow to bounce on the string until it comes to rest naturally.

    (b. 23) Rapidly alternate between two given pitches but gradually decrease in speed over duration given.

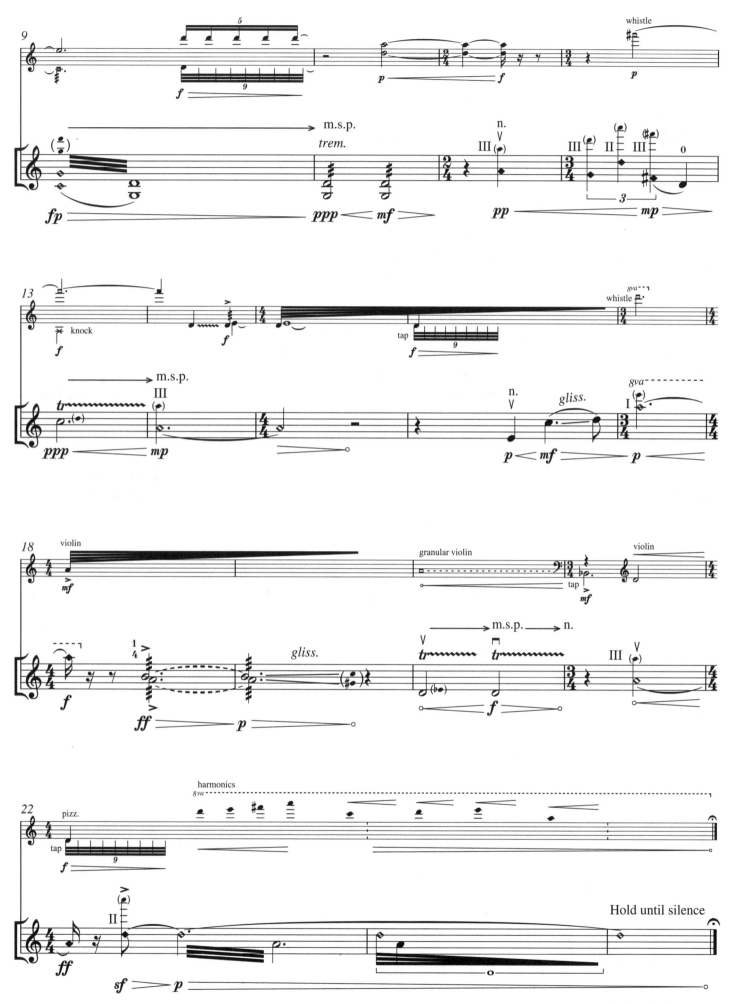

London, 20 August 2007

Canto

HELEN GRIME

The composer has written: 'Canto, meaning song or melody, should be played expressively and with rubato. The mood is reflective and melancholy with a passionate climax reached at bar 13. The piano and violin are of equal importance throughout; the dynamics reflect when a particular passage should come to the fore. The grace notes should be before the beat and may be played as freely as desired.'

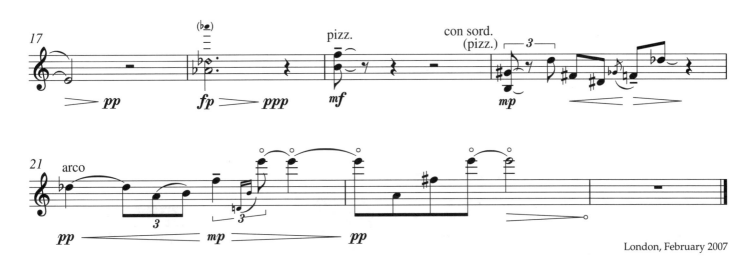

London, February 2007

for Alexandra Wood

An Implausible Tale
(with moral)

KENNETH HESKETH

The composer has written: 'The various character indications in this work (*ruvido, con amore, minaccioso* etc.) should give the player a good idea of how to portray the differing aspects. The style should be that of a storyteller speaking to a small and intimate audience and as with any moral tale should instil moral rectitude. It is the main protagonist who comes off worse!'

Più mosso ♩ = 126

ff

gliss.

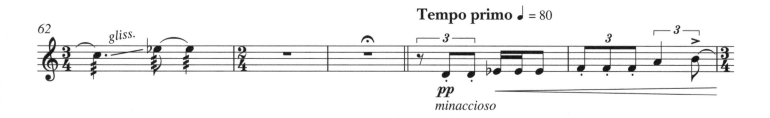

Tempo primo ♩ = 80

pp
minaccioso

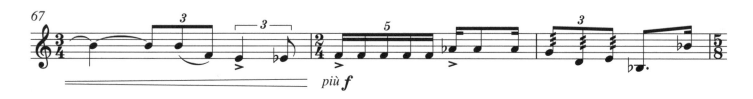

più ***f***

MORAL

Poco meno mosso, inquieto

♩ = 66

p

pp *lontano, spettrale*

London, March 2007

Moto ascendente

DANIEL GIORGETTI

The composer has written: 'Moto ascendente translates as "upward movement". This refers to the register of the violin becoming gradually higher as the music progresses. Although the piece begins *piano*, the rhythm of the violin needs to be clearly audible from the very first bar as there should be a strong sense of the music's energy potential right from the start. The piano's sustain pedal should be released the moment the last violin note has been played.'

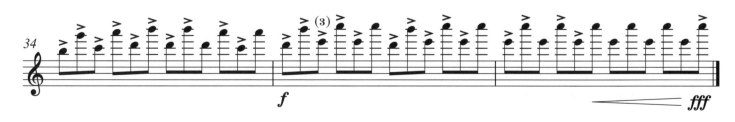

London, April 2007

The Egrets have Landed

THEA MUSGRAVE

Playa del Rey, California,
15 June–5 July 2007

The composer has written: 'Immediately north of the busy Los Angeles airport which serves a gigantic city, right beside the vast Pacific Ocean, there is a small, peaceful lagoon. Every day egrets fly in and land on its sunlit banks in a whirl of white plumage.'

AB 3453

The Fifth String

for violin and soundtrack

JOÃO PEDRO OLIVEIRA

The composer has written: 'This piece is about interaction between the violin and the electronic sounds on the soundtrack. These electronic sounds create a separate part played on an imaginary "fifth string", which can make sounds that the violin cannot make. The soundtrack part is notated as precisely as possible so the performer can see as well as hear what the soundtrack is playing and interact with it almost as if it were a "live" second instrument.'

Performance directions

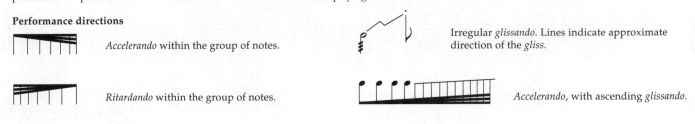

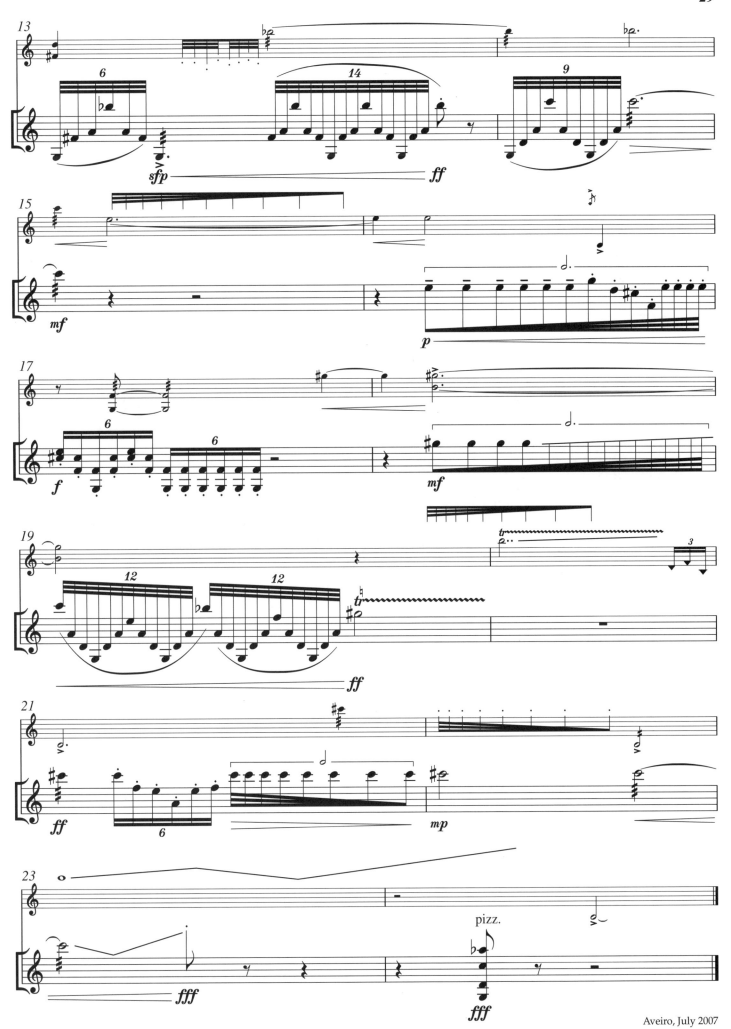

Aveiro, July 2007

CD TRACK LISTING

1	David Sawer	*A Fork in the Road*	1:13
2	Michael Zev Gordon	*Joshi's Dance*	1:13
3	David Matthews	*An Alpine Tune*	1:11
4	Philip Cashian	*Forgotten Game*	1:06
5	Howard Skempton	*Arietta*	1:33
6	Timothy Salter	*Daydream*	1:43
7	Dobrinka Tabakova	*Lydian River*	2:24
8	Tansy Davies	*Woodman's Echo*	1:46
9	Hugh Wood	*Bagatelle*	0:54
10	Huw Watkins	*Sarabande*	1:45
11	Patrick Nunn	*Collage on D*	1:38
12	Helen Grime	*Canto*	2:12
13	Kenneth Hesketh	*An Implausible Tale (with moral)*	2:44
14	Daniel Giorgetti	*Moto ascendente*	1:19
15	Thea Musgrave	*The Egrets have Landed*	1:46
16	João Pedro Oliveira	*The Fifth String*	1:56

Accompanying soundtracks

	Patrick Nunn	*Collage on D*	
17	soundtrack only		1:45
18	soundtrack with pulse, for practice purposes		1:45
	João Pedro Oliveira	*The Fifth String*	
19	soundtrack only		1:49
20	soundtrack with pulse, for practice purposes		1:49

Violin **Alexandra Wood**

Piano **Thalia Myers**

Co-Producer **Leslie East**

Co-Producer and Recording Engineer **Ken Blair**

Recorded on 28 and 29 April 2009 in The Menuhin Hall, Yehudi Menuhin School, Stoke d'Abernon, Surrey
A BMP Production for ABRSM (Publishing) Ltd